It's Party Time!

W9-BNS-118

PaRRagon

Bath · New York · Singapore · Hong Kong · Cologne · Delhi
Melbourne · Amsterdam · Johannesburg · Auckland · Shenzhen

Pages 6-7

Pages 10-11

Pages 22-23

Page 14-15

Pages 22-23

Page 12

Pages 18-19

Pages 28-29

Page 19

How to Use This Book

 Read the story, all about Luke going to his first birthday party.

 Look at each picture in the story closely. You may be asked to find or count things in a scene and place a sticker on the page.

 Try each activity as you go along, or read the story first, then go back and do the activities. The answers are at the bottom of each activity page.

 Some pictures will need stickers to finish the scenes or activities. Any leftover stickers can be used to decorate the book or your things.

Luke has something special in the mail today.
It's an invitation from his friend Hannah.

Can you find these things in the kitchen?

6

She is having a birthday party,
and she wants Luke to come!

How many envelopes are on the table?

Now place your cat sticker here.

Mom and Luke go shopping.
First, they pick a card for Hannah.

8

Which two pieces complete the picture below?

a

b

c

d

Answer: pieces b and d

9

Then they look for a birthday present for Hannah.
"Hannah likes dinosaurs," Luke tells Mom.

Find three stickers to finish the picture.

Can you find these things in the store?

They find a coloring book with lots of dinosaur pictures. "Hannah will like that," Luke says.

Now place the sticker of Luke here.

At home, Mom helps Luke wrap Hannah's book and the paint set they bought to go with it.

They tie it with a bright yellow ribbon. "I can't wait to give Hannah her present!" Luke says.

Look at the presents below.
Find one in each row that is different from the other two.

Answer:

It's the day
of the party.
Mom and Luke pick
up Luke's friend
Holly on the way.
Help them find the
way to Hannah's
house.

Answer:

Hannah and her mom greet
Luke and Holly at the door.

"Thank you," says Hannah, when Luke
gives her the present he has brought.

Can you spot five differences between this picture and the one opposite?

Answer:

Hannah's living room is decorated with balloons and a big birthday banner.

Find the sticker to complete the picture.

Happy Birthday, Hannah!

Can you find these things in the picture?

Luke's friends Sam, Emily, and Holly are at the party, too. They all say hello to Luke and Holly.

Now place the sticker of Hannah here.

It's time for some party games! The children play "Pin the Tail on the Dinosaur."

How many blue party hats can you see?

Can you help Luke pin the tail on the dinosaur? Follow the tangled lines to get to the poster.

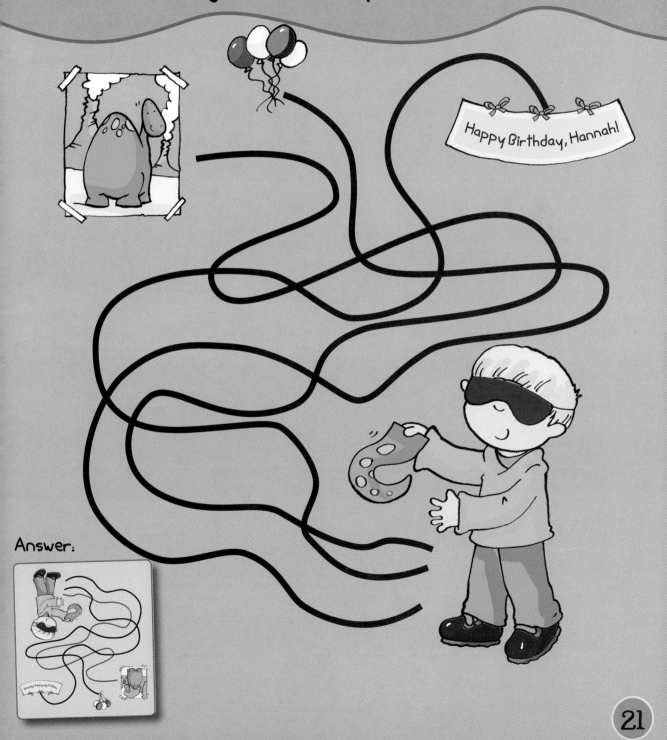

Happy Birthday, Hannah!

Answer:

After the games, everyone is hungry. Good thing it's time for Hannah's birthday lunch!

Can you find these things in the picture?

Find the stickers to finish the picture.

They all sit at the table. There are lots of yummy things to eat.

Now place the sticker of Luke here.

Hannah's mom brings in the birthday cake, and everyone sings "Happy Birthday."

Hannah makes a wish and blows out all the candles.

Find the two pictures of the cake that are exactly the same.

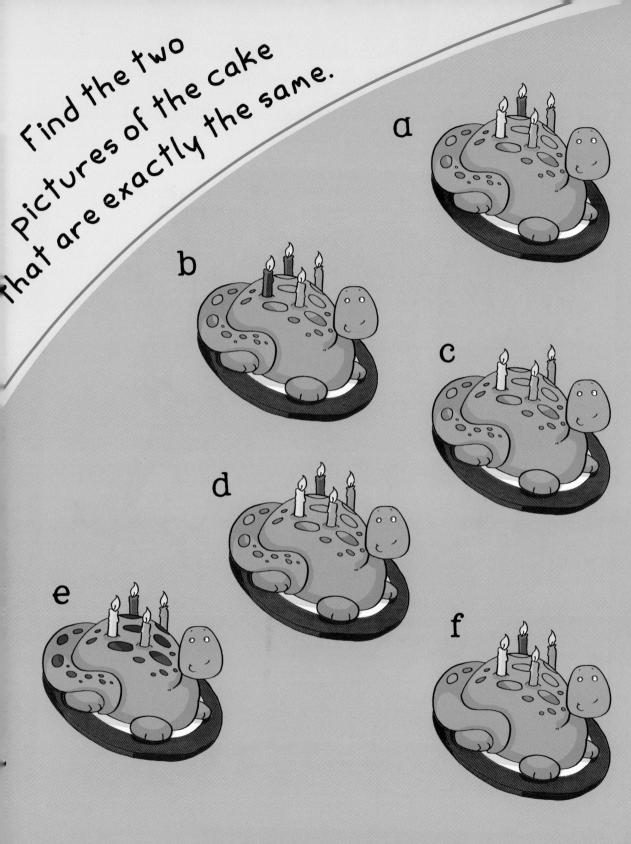

a

b

c

d

e

f

Hannah opens her presents. She loves the book and paint set from Luke. "Thank you, Luke," she says. "Thank you, everyone."

How many presents does Hannah have left to open?

Match Hannah's presents to their shadows.

Answer:

Hannah's dad has a surprise for everyone.
He will make balloon animals for them!

What color is the picture frame?

Can you find these things in the picture?

Hannah gets a dinosaur, of course!
Luke asks for an elephant.

Happy Birthday, Hannah!

Now place the sticker of Luke's elephant here.

Party time is over. Hannah's mom gives Luke a goody bag to take home. Luke thanks Hannah for inviting him to her party.

"It's my birthday soon," he tells her, "and I hope you will come to my party, too!"